The **IF...** Chronicles

By the same author
Maggie's Farm (Penguin)
Further down on Maggie's Farm (Penguin)

The IF... Chronicles

Steve Bell

Methuen

This collection first published
in book form in 1983
by Methuen London Ltd,
11 New Fetter Lane, London EC4P 4EE

The strips originally published by *The Guardian*, 1982, 1983

Designed by Brian Homer
Edited by Steve Bell and Brian Homer

Printed in Great Britain
by Richard Clay (The Chaucer Press) Ltd
Bungay, Suffolk

ISBN 0 413 53970 9

For Heather, William (and the B.)

Introduction

Evenin' all!

So you've bought this book, have you? I've had my eye on people like you for some time. Something tells me that you're not the sort of people that have my boys' true interests at heart. You're the sort who'd complain about my boys having a little innocent bazooka practice, and then come whining to us when you get lost or when your cat gets stuck up a tree. Just what do you take us for? Public Servants??!! You'd better wise up right away, because the Force is coming off the fence.

For too long we've stood by while the real villains in this society have got away with murder. That's all over now. We are aiming to tear out subversion at the roots. Henceforth, should anyone even mention socialism in any primary school across the land, my boys will be there. In minutes. In strength. Because we've finally got you namby-pamby lesbian Trotskyist social-working woolly-hatted ethnic pacifist nursery school teaching dupes of the Kremlin taped! So don't try anything funny.

Mind how you go.

GRH Courage

Gerald 'Badger' Courage
Chief Constable

It is summer 1982. Ron is visiting his friend, Liz.

IF....

YOUR MAJESTY... AS ONE HEAD OF STATE TO ANOTHER, I WOULD LIKE TO TAKE THIS OPPORTUNITY TO SAY...

UUURRM... COULD YOU SLOW DOWN A MOMENT THERE, YOUR HOLINESS!!

I'M SORRY, SIR,.. THE IDIOT CARDS SEEM TO HAVE GOT MIXED UP!

YOUR MAJESTY - AS ONE HEAD OF STATE TO ANOTHER I WOULD LIKE TO TAKE THIS OPP-ORTUNITY TO SAY..

DID YOU EVER HEAR THE ONE ABOUT THE MONARCH AND THE NOSEBAG?

EL SALVADOR A NEAT PLACE FOR A STATE VISIT

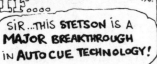

IF....   196.

SIR...THIS STETSON IS A MAJOR BREAKTHROUGH IN AUTOCUE TECHNOLOGY!

YOW!

...A MINIATURISED T.V. SCREEN IS CONCEALED INSIDE THE HAT. THE T.V. IMAGE OF THE TEXT OF YOUR SPEECH IS PROJECTED ONTO AN INVISIBLE MEMBRANE IN FRONT OF YOUR FACE.....

...YOU SIMPLY READ IT OUT, WHICH SAVES UNNECESSARY WORRY, AND ENABLES YOU TO CONCENTRATE ON SOUNDING SINCERE AND LOOKING RELAXED AS ONLY YOU CAN, MR. PRESIDENT!

WANNA GO BYE-BYES NOW, DOUCHEBAG!

IF....

TESTING.... A ONE A TWO A THREE A FOUR.... *DONK DONK*

"Friends, what I want to talk to you about today is the threat to humanity that is presented to us today by the Spectre...."

"...of a completely brainless bimbo in a cowboy hat. Yes, friends, I'm talking about myself. I am so brainless I am not even aware of what I am saying to you at this moment in time!"

— Steve Bell —

HEY, **DOUCHEBAG!!** THIS **AUTOCUE-HAT** WORKS LIKE A **DREAM!** I DON'T KNOW WHAT I WAS **SAYING,** BUT IT **FELT GREAT!!**

IF....

"...so I'm prepared to say **this** to the **Soviets** in all sincerity......"

OH MY **GAAHD!!** A SUDDEN BREEZE HAS **BLOWN** MY **AUTOCUE-HAT OFF!!**

OH MY **GAAAHD!!** **WHAT** AM I GONNA **SAY?** I'D **BETTER PRAY** FOR **INSPIRATION!**

— Steve Bell —

BACK OFF, YA BIG RED SCHMUCKS! THERE'S ONLY ROOM FOR **ONE** TOP BANANA IN THE BUNCH!!

YEA! YOWSA! YEE HA!

YAY, HE HAS THE VERITABLE GIFT OF TONGUES!!

IF....

SIR... THERE HAVE BEEN A LARGE NUMBER OF COMPLAINTS THAT YOU'RE **NOT ENTIRELY RESPONSIBLE** FOR YOUR **OWN WORDS AND ACTIONS**....

...PEOPLE DO SAY THAT YOU DEPEND **TOO HEAVILY** ON **AUTOCUES** AND ON **SLICK** PRESENTATION TECHNIQUES. THERE IS EVEN TALK THAT YOU ARE A **FRONT MAN** FOR A NAMELESS "**MR. BIG**" WHO PULLS ALL THE **STRINGS**. YOU MUST **PROVE** THEM **WRONG**, MR. PRESIDENT, YOU **MUST** GIVE A SPEECH **WITHOUT AIDS OF ANY KIND!!**

199

FRIENDS....

— Steve Bell —

WE GOTTA **GOMB** THOSE **GARGARIAN GOLSHEVIK GASTARDS** TO **GUGGERY**... ...**GOTTLE OF GEER, GOTTLE OF GEER**...

IF ...I FEEL **GOOD** ABOUT MYSELF, DOUCHEBAG.. IT'S **GREAT** TO BE **HOME** AGAIN!!

200.

I THINK I CAME OVER **WELL** IN **EUROPE**, DON'T YOU AGREE, DOUCHEBAG?

SURELY SIR

...I THINK THAT THANKS TO MY SPEECHMAKING HARDWARE, PEOPLE WERE **IMPRESSED** BY MY **NATURALNESS + SINCERITY**

THAT'S A FACT SIR

I STILL THINK YOU'RE A **SERIOUSLY DELUDED** HALF-WIT **BOZO**, RON!

— Steve Bell —

IF... WELL, KIPLING, IT SEEMS THAT **VICTORY** IS **OURS!!** JOHNNY GAUCHO HAS THROWN IN HIS **PONCHO** AT LAST!

A TRIUMPHANT **VINDICATION** OF OUR **PRINCIPLED STAND!**

THE MESSAGE HAS GONE OUT **LOUD** AND **CLEAR** TO EVERY **TINPOT DICTATOR** ACROSS THE GLOBE: "**HANDS OFF THE BRITISH LION!**—HE MAY BE **OLD**, HE MAY BE **SLOW TO ROUSE**, BUT WHEN IT COMES TO THE **CRUNCH**...

201.

...HE'S STILL A **BLOOD-THIRSTY MOTH-EATEN PSYCHOPATH!!"**

YOU'RE A TREACHEROUS CYNICAL BOUNDER, KIPLING!

IF... THIS HAS BEEN A TIME OF GENUINE **HEROISM**, KIPLING. IN FUTURE, PEOPLE WILL LOOK TO **THIS PERIOD** FOR **INSPIRATION**...

...A TIME WHEN OUR OPTIONS WERE **CLEAR CUT**; WHEN WE QUITE SIMPLY **DID** WHAT **HAD** TO BE DONE!

YOU KNOW, KIPLING, **WAR** HAS A LOT OF **DRAWBACKS** BUT IT CERTAINLY DOES **BRING PEOPLE TOGETHER**. WE BURY OUR DIFFERENCES AND **UNITE** AGAINST THE **COMMON FOE!!**

♪ THE **PARTY'S OV-ER**... ♪ IT'S TIME TO **CALL IT A DA-A-Y**... ♪

202.

STUPID BLOODY BIRD!

9

13

IF.... I SHOWED THAT **NO-COUNT PUNK HAIG**, DOUCHEBAG— —NOW HE KNOWS WHO THE **REAL TOP BANANA** IS!

THAT'S **GREAT**, CHIEF BUT **WHO'S** GOING TO REPLACE HIM??

THE ONE I HAVE IN MIND IS HONEST, RELIABLE, AND **ONE HUNDRED PERCENT PATRIOTIC AMERICAN!!**

DOUCHEBAG, I'D LIKE YOU TO MEET **FRANCIS** THE **TALKING MULE!**

HOWDY!

IF... THIS **LEBANESE PROBLEM** IS ONE **TOUGH TORTILLA** GENTLEMEN....

...AS I PERCEIVE IT, WE CAN EITHER LEAVE IT TO THE **ISRAELIS** TO **BLOW** EVERYTHING TO **POOP**....

...OR WE CAN SEND IN THE **MARINES**. WHADDYA SAY, MEN?

YIBBLE YIBBLE

HOWDY HOWDY

IT FEELS **GOOD** TO KNOW WE'RE ALL **TOGETHER** ON THIS ONE!

IFoooo

HOWDY

IT FEELS **GOOD** TO KNOW THAT THINGS ARE **UNDER CONTROL** AGAIN!

Steve Bell —

I FEEL LIKE I CAN **RELAX AGAIN!**

HOWDY

WITH A **TEAM** LIKE I'VE GOT I CAN **GO BYE-BYES** WITH AN **EASY MIND**

FRANCIS — THAT'S **NOT** THE WAY MY **SECRETARY** OF STATE SHOULD TREAT THE **FLAG!!**

IF...

OK MEN, TODAY WE'RE GONNA **TALK TURKEY** ABOUT ONE OF THE **PREMIER PROBLEM POTATOES** OF OUR TIME....

HOWDY!

...TODAY WE'RE GONNA **TURN OUR MINDS** TO **YOORP!**

—Steve Bell—

TURN OUR MINDS TO **WHAT**, MR. PRESIDENT??

TO **YOORP** YOU **DUMBOS**, TO **YOORP!!**

HOWDY DOODY?

COME ON YOU **JOKERS**, YOU'RE **PUTTIN' ME ON!** **YOORP** IS ACROSS THE **ATLANTIC** — IT'S **ABOVE AFRICA** AND **NEXT TO ASIA!!**

RIGHT!

HOWDY?

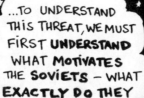

The Penguin
Hatched Port Grantham,
Falkland Islands 1926

Having spent his early years
in traditional Penguin
pursuits, the Penguin
became disaffected with the
prevailing colonialist ethic in
the rookery and dropped out.
After a brief spell as a guano
smuggler, he got a job as a
lookout for a firm of
Argentinian scrap dealers.
   With the arrival of the
Task Force he joined the
Royal Navy on an informal
freelance basis, befriending
Able Seaman Reg Kipling,
crewman on the armoured
nuclear punt HMS
'Incredible', who ultimately
helped to smuggle the
Penguin into Great Britain as
an illegal black & white
immigrant. Since then he
has been on the run. His
interests include show
business, tap-dancing and
fish.

18

IF...

You'll be hearing from us, Kipling you blighter!

Yo ho ho!! Phthaaarrp?!

Yo ho ho!! Freedom!!! Yip yip yip!!

Yee hee hee!! Stuff the Navy!!!

Yo ho ho ho hum...

DHSS

IF... Madam, you can rest assured that no intruder could get past the pressure sensitive alarm beneath the floorboards!

Hmmm!

...And even if the unthinkable should happen, and an intruder should penetrate this far, there is a fail-safe device which ensures they will get no further!

...The floor opens and they are projected into a pit of Tebbits!

Good Lord!

I'm impressed!

Ig! Ig!

Gah!

Where on Earth did that penguin come from? ?!??!!

226

IF... HORRIFYING! HORRIFYING!!

ARE YOU TALKING ABOUT THE APPALLINGLY **LAX** SECURITY SURROUNDING OUR **LEADER**, HARRY?

EVENING ABCESS
PRIME MINISTER BITTEN BY PENGUIN IN OWN LIVING-ROOM SCANDAL

NO, I'M TALKING ABOUT THESE **BIRD-LOVERS** IN POSITIONS OF RESPONS-IBILITY!....YEEEUGGH!! I'M NOT **PREJUDICED**, BUT THEY MAKE ME **SHUDDER**!!

NEW **STOAT**
POLICE CHIEF HAD PROLONGED RELATION-SHIP WITH PARROT

-229.

...WHICH IS WHY I'M SENDING **YOU** OUT TO FIND THE **PENGUIN** AND **INTERVIEW** IT!!

HOW TO SPOT A **BIRD-LOVER** IN YOUR **ORGANISATION:**
TELL-TALE SIGNS → SWOOP SWOOP

IF... PSSST!

SWOOP

230.

EVENING! – I WAS TOLD I MIGHT FIND YOU HERE.... I WONDERED IF YOU'D MIND ANSWERING A FEW **QUESTIONS**?

SORRY, MATEY – I'VE ALREADY **SOLD** MY STORY TO THE '**SUN**'!!

GIT AHT!

24

IF... 237.

I'M **BORED** — WHEN IS THE 'SUN' GOING TO **PRINT** MY STORY?

ALL IN GOOD TIME, JOHN..

WHEN IS THE WORLD GOING TO BE **TOLD** ABOUT THE **WEB** OF **TREACHERY, INTRIGUE** AND **DECEPTION** THAT LEADS TO THE **VERY HIGHEST LEVELS** OF **GOVERNMENT**?!!

ALL IN GOOD TIME, JOHN

WHEN IS THE SORDID **NETWORK OF CORRUPTION** ALL THE WAY UP THE **POLICE FORCE** GOING TO BE REVEALED IN **ALL ITS SHABBY GLORY**?!!!

ALL IN GOOD TIME, JOHN

MY NAME'S **NOT** 'JOHN'! — AND WHERE'S THE **"HALF TON OF FISH UP FRONT"** I WAS PROMISED??

— Steve Bell —

IF... 238.

THAT **BIG SWINE** BLEW THE **GAFFE** ON ME!!

MY FRIENDS'LL GET YOU FOR THIS, YOU BIG CHICKEN-SUITED MORON

OH YEAH? PULL THE OTHER ONE, JOHN

I **TRUSTED** YOU — I THOUGHT YOU WERE ONE OF US!!

TRY NOT TO MAKE A FUSS, JOHN

SLEEK

BANZAI!

— Steve Bell —

IF...

PEOPLE LIKE **YOU** MAKE ME SICK!...

YOU'D SELL **Y**OUR **OWN** GRANDMOTHER INTO SLAVERY IF IT SUITED YOUR PURPOSES. YOU'RE **WHOLLY AMORAL!!**

COME AGAIN JOHN?

AND **THICK** WITH IT!...

...WHAT I'M SAYING IS-- YOU COULDN'T **GIVE** A **MONKEY'S** ABOUT **ANYTHING** OR **ANYONE !!!**

@☆※ WATCH IT, JOHN!

239.

MONKEYS? IS SOMEBODY OFFERING MONKEYS?

?

IF...

YOU DID SAY "MONKEYS" DIDN'T YOU?

CHIEF CONSTABLE-- -I'M DEEPLY SHOCKED!

240

DO YOU MEAN THAT FOR A SUM AS **PALTRY** AS **FIVE HUNDRED POUNDS** YOU'RE PREPARED TO **JEOPARDISE** YOUR **OWN** CAREER, AS WELL AS THE **GOOD NAME** OF THE **VERY FORCE** YOU'VE **DEDICATED** YOUR **LIFE** TO ??

...YOU'RE **CORRUPT** CHIEF CONSTABLE!!

NO....I'M JUST VERY FOND OF MONKEYS

26

IF... YOU'RE AN **ILLEGAL ALIEN**, AND ON TOP OF THAT...

...YOU'RE **CHARGED** WITH **CONSPIRING** TO UNLAWFULLY **BITE THE PERSON** OF THE **PRIME MINISTER**.

DO YOU WISH TO MAKE A **STATEMENT?** HAVE YOU **ANYTHING AT ALL** YOU WISH TO SAY??

YES.....SHE TASTED RUSTY, AND I THINK I BROKE THIS TOOTH ON A RIVET

IF... "**PENGUIN** UP BEFORE **THE BEAK!**"—THIS IS INDEED A **TURN-UP** FOR THE **BOOKS!!**

SILENCE IN COURT!

BEFORE I PASS SENTENCE, IS THERE **ANYTHING** YOU WISH TO SAY TO THE COURT?

YES, THERE IS....

IF I OFFERED YOU EACH A **MONKEY**, UP FRONT, IN YOUR HAND RIGHT NOW, WHAT WOULD YOU **SAY**??

IF YOU THINK **BRIBERY** WILL HELP YOUR CAUSE NOW, YOU ARE SADLY MISTAKEN!

?

Steve Bell

IG!

BOING!

THAT'S WHAT I THOUGHT!

29

30

Francis the Talking Mule

Born Rio Grantham, New Mexico 1926

After spending his early years as a pack mule in the US Army, Francis the Talking Mule shot to fame in a series of unique films during the 1940s. Many years later, while forming his administration, Ronald Reagan, in search of someone with military experience who would bring a forthright approach to foreign affairs, made Francis National Security Adviser and later Secretary of State, replacing Alexander Haig.

With his linguistic gifts, his resolute stance in negotiations and his capacity for oats, Francis the Talking Mule has left his clear imprint on American foreign policy. His interests include gambling and fast cars.

IF...

SIR! FRANCIS HERE WOULD LIKE TO ASK YOU A QUESTION...

HOWDY

WHADDYA WANT MULE??

...FRANCIS WOULD LIKE TO KNOW: WHO IS THE MOST POWERFUL MAN ON EARTH??

BZZBZZ PSSZZ

I'M GLAD YOU ASKED THAT, FRANK...

SINCE I PERSONALLY CONTROL THE LARGEST AND MOST ADVANCED COLLECTION OF BIG ONES THE WORLD HAS EVER SEEN, I AM PROBABLY THE MOST POWERFUL MAN ON EARTH!!

HE WANTS TO KNOW IF THAT MAKES HIM THE MOST POWERFUL MULE ON EARTH?

SURE, WHY NOT?

249

IF...

MR. PRESIDENT.... ...FRANCIS WOULD LIKE TO KNOW WHAT EXACTLY YOU MEAN BY "BIG ONES"??

SURE THING, FRANK

"BIG ONES" ARE THE BASIS OF ALL OUR POLICIES! BIG ONES ARE OUR MAIN DEFENSE AGAINST THE GODLESS COMMIE HORDE! THE MORE BIG ONES WE HAVE, THE SAFER WE ARE!

YOWSA!

250.

THE WAY I SEE IT — IF A MAN AIN'T GOT A BIG ONE, THEN HOW IS HE GONNA STAND UP FOR WHAT'S HIS?? IF SOME OTHER CREEP COMES AT YOU WITH A BIG ONE AND YOU'VE ONLY GOT A LITTLE ONE, OR WORSE — IF YOU HAVEN'T GOT ONE AT ALL — WHAT ARE YOU GONNA DO?? IF YOU LIVE LIKE A PUNK, THEN PEOPLE ARE GONNA TREAT YOU LIKE A PUNK!!

TAP TAP

FRANCIS SAYS THAT AS A MULE, HE CAN REALLY RELATE TO WHAT YOU'RE SAYING...

HOWDY

GOOD TO HEAR THAT, FRANK!

32

IF...

NOW I'D LIKE YOU TO EXAMINE THESE FIGURES CAREFULLY...

263

...THEY SHOW THE **BASIC PAY** OF THE AVERAGE HEALTH WORKER OVER THE PAST TEN YEARS....

...NOW I THINK YOU'LL AGREE WITH ME WHEN I SAY THAT ONLY A **CHICKEN** COULD **SURVIVE** ON **THAT KIND OF MONEY**....

WE **AGREE** WITH YOU **ABSOLUTELY**, FOWLMAN!

LOGICALLY, THEREFORE, YOU ARE **ALL POULTRY,** AND THIS IS MY **FINAL OFFER!!**

SWOOP

IS THIS MAN BRAIN-DEAD?

IF...

FOWLMAN — I'M **IMPRESSED** BY THE WAY YOU'RE HANDLING THIS **HEALTH SERVICE BUSINESS**..

— Steve Bell —

ONLY **TOO HAPPY** TO BE OF SERVICE, MA'AM....

I **LIKE** YOUR **STYLE,** FOWLMAN — YOU'RE HANDLING A **DIFFICULT PROBLEM** WITH **SILVERY-TONGUED EFFICIENCY!**

THANK YOU, MA'AM — MY ONLY AIM IS TO PLEASE!

BY THE WAY, THERE'S A **BLOCKED TOILET** I'D LIKE YOU TO DEAL WITH ON YOUR WAY OUT....

264

IF... — Steve Bell —

WHERE DO WE GO FROM HERE, FOWLMAN?

DON'T BUG ME NOW!

..BUT, **HELL'S TEETH**, FOWLMAN — I CAN'T STAND THE **HATRED** AND **CONTEMPT** I GET WHENEVER PEOPLE FIND OUT THAT I'M ONE OF YOUR **FOLLOWERS**!!...

...OLD LADIES **SPIT** AT ME IN THE STREET — MY OWN **MOTHER** WON'T **SPEAK** TO ME ANY MORE! — I CAN'T **STAND** IT FOWLMAN!!

SO.... IT'S **TOUGH** ALL OVER — YOU'RE **BREAKING** MY **HEART**!!

I'M **SERIOUS**, FOWLMAN! THIS IS **IT**! I'M **GIVING UP**!! I'M **CUTTING LOOSE**!!!

265.

CHICKEN OUT ON ME, WOULD YOU??

IF... NOW **HEAR THIS** YOU **PUNKS** — YOU'VE **HAD** MY **FINAL OFFER** — YOU'RE JUST **WASTING** YOUR **OWN** TIME AND **MINE**!

12%

NHS 12%

12% NOW

I AM **ADAMANT** IN THIS AND IF THE **STIFFS** START **PILING UP** IN THE STREET **REMEMBER** — THESE WILL BE **ENTIRELY** YOUR **OWN RESPONSIBILITY**!

I SPEAK FOR 90% OF THE **RIGHT-THINKING** PEOPLE OF THIS COUNTRY WHEN I SAY.... **NYUUURRGH!!**

FOWLPEST?

QUICK!! RING FOR COLONEL SANDERS!!

— 266

— Steve Bell

AWK!

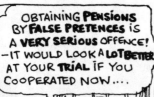

Harry Hardnose
Born Grantham, Lincs 1926

'Harry the Bastard' entered the world of journalism as an obscene messenger boy at the offices of the 'Morning Mule' in 1939. Through a unique personal system of blackmail and extortion, Harry rose to become Booze and Fags correspondent on the short lived 'Mule' Gents' Page. From there it was but a short step to his present position as News Editor on the 'Mule On Sunday'. His interests include telling lies, drinking, smoking and the SDP.

45

46

IF...

IT'S A **GREAT HONOUR** TO MEET YOU, MA'AM...

...I'VE HEARD SO MUCH ABOUT **YOU** AND **YOUR CABINET!!**

279.

....THERE **ONE THING** I'VE ALWAYS WANTED TO ASK YOU....

- Steve Bell -

...CAN **NORMAN TEBBIT** REALLY **CRACK WALNUTS** WITH HIS **EYELIDS?**

HAIL

TELL ALL!

IF...

WHAT'S YOUR **POISON**, MR THATCHER SIR?

LARGE G. AND T. PLEASE!!

♪ IN WITH THE **G.** IN WITH THE **T.** ♪ TWIST OF LEMON-FIDDLE-DE-DEE!

YOU'RE A **CLEVER** LITTLE BLIGHTER!

...VOILÀ – THE **PERFECT** G. AND T.!

YOU'RE A **DAMNED INSPIRED** LITTLE BLIGHTER!

Steve Bell -

286

...SO THERE WE WERE AT THE **NINETEENTH HOLE** WITH **FUZZIES** ON EVERY **SIDE!** "HOLD FIRE TILL YOU SEE THE **WHITES** OF **THEIR EYES, LAD!**" -SLURP SLURP!!!

STEADY ON THERE CHAPPIE!

IF... Steve Bell

RRRRR!

I DON'T CARE WHAT YOU SAY, MAG — I DON'T ALTOGETHER TRUST THAT LITTLE TIN BLIGHTER!

287.

NONSENSE, DENIS! NOW, TELL ME HONESTLY WHAT YOU THINK OF MY NEW CONFERENCE HAT?

RRRRRR!

CRUISE

I...I...I..ER...

IT IS ABSOLUTELY THE MOST SUBLIME CREATION EVER TO GRACE THE HEAD OF A WORLD LEADER MA'AM!

I...I..I..ER... SSSSLP...

IF...

I WANT A DAMNED GOOD SPEECH THIS YEAR, ROBOT!

ABSOLUTELY MA'AM!! BIP BIP BIP...

I WANT A REALLY GOOD CATCHPHRASE THIS YEAR! NOW LET'S SEE — WE'VE HAD "REALISM AND RESPONSIBILITY" "FORWARD TOGETHER" AND "WINNING THROUGH" — WHAT HAVE YOU COME UP WITH, ROBOT??

ZIK ZIKKA ZIKKA BLEEP!

CHURN

288.

— Steve Bell —

AHHH... I SEE YOU'VE GIVEN ME A CHOICE! — I APPRECIATE THAT.

YIK YIK YIK

...SO IT'S EITHER: "CRAWL, YOU SCUM!" OR "NEXT STOP, OBLIVION."

ZIK ZIKKA CHAK CHAK CHAK

VOMIT

52

IF...

NEXT STOP, OBLIVION

—Steve Bell—

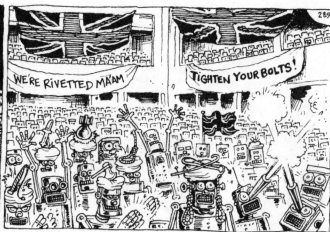

289.

WE'RE RIVETTED MA'AM

TIGHTEN YOUR BOLTS!

IF... —Steve Bell—

WELL, THAT'S ANOTHER TRIUMPHANT CONFERENCE OVER FOR ANOTHER YEAR!!

MAG 1

290.

YOU'LL BE ABLE TO GIVE THE LITTLE TIN CHAP A REST NOW, EH, MAG??

WHAT?! GIVE UP MY CLOSEST ADVISER? CERTAINLY NOT!!

PUBLIC FOOTPATH

MAG 1

MY THINK TANK IS AN ABIDING SOURCE OF STIMULATING NEW IDEAS! ROBOT — WHY DON'T YOU TELL DENIS YOUR LATEST SUGGESTION?

ABSOLUTELY, MA'AM!

ANY MORE BACKCHAT FROM YOU, FOUR EYES AND YOU'RE GOING TO GET A TARMAC OVERCOAT!

54

Reg Kipling
Born Grantham, Lincs 1926

Former Able Seaman and member of the elite Special Punt Service, trained in one hundred ways to kill flies, he served on the armoured nuclear punt HMS 'Incredible'. He became seriously disaffected during the Falklands campaign, a feeling which was exacerbated by contact with the Penguin.

On returning to Great Britain he was dishonourably discharged from the navy and joined the ranks of the unemployed. His interests include prison reform and penguinology.

IF₀₀₀

Knock! Knock!

WHAT'S THIS AREA **CALLED**, MR. KIPLING?

XANADU? NIRVANA? HAMBURGER HEAVEN?

NO, THOSE ARE JUST THE NAMES OF SHOPS

Steve Bell

303

THIS IS....**PECKHAM!**

OK I'VE **PECKED** THEM — NOW **WHAT DID YOU** SAY THIS PLACE WAS **CALLED**??

IF₀₀₀

304

OH I SEE! THERE'S A **BY-ELECTION** HERE THE DAY AFTER TOMORROW!

DON'T YOU BE **TAKEN IN** BY ANY OF THIS **DIVERSIONARY BOURGEOIS OBFUS-CATION**, MR KIPLING!

NO, I WAS GOING TO VOTE **LABOUR**

NONSENSE, MAN — **WHOEVER** YOU VOTE FOR, **THE BOURGEOIS** WILL CONTINUE TO **HOLD SWAY!** THE **LABOUR PARTY** IS **HISTORICALLY** AN INSTRU-MENT FOR **CONTAINING** AND **DEFUSING** ANY **REAL** OPPOSITION TO **BOURGEOIS HEGEMONY!**

TAKE MY ADVICE, MR. KIPLING — BE PRAGMATIC — VOTE FOR THE ONE THAT'S OFFERING **FREE FISH, UPFRONT, IN YOUR HAND, NOW!**

COBBLERS!

61

IF... PORTENTOUS 438 PART SERIAL STARTS TODAY...

BUZBY'S PEOPLE

INTRODUCING:

PYOTR LEFLEGIN AND HIS SECRET WHEELBARROW

CHELTENHAM — THE ENTRANCE TO THE SECRET GOVERNMENT COMMUNICATIONS H.Q.....

SECURITY

ALL PASSES MUST BE SHOWN

OI! YOU WITH THE WHEELBARROW!

PLEASE —, I YAM CLEANING LADY

WHAT'S ALL THE HARDWARE FOR THEN, EH?

PASS

309.

THANKS TO PAUL STEVENS —

I YAM ALSO PONK ROCKER

PASS, FRIEND!

© Steve Bell — 1982

IF... SECRET GOV'T COMMUNICATIONS HEADQUATERS

EXCUSE, PLEASE; I LOOK FOR MR. BIGFISH?

TRY THE THIRD DOOR ON THE RIGHT

TOP SECRET / SECRET / SECRET / SECRET / SECRET / SECRET / SECRET / SECRET

310. © Steve Bell

MR. BIGFISH? ARE YOU YIN THERE MEESTER FISH??

WHAT IF I AM? WHAT DO YOU CARE? WHAT DO I CARE?

THIS IS BRIAN WIDLAKE WITH SEVEN HOURS OF NEWS

...WHAT DOES ANYONE CARE? HAVE YOU GOT A CURE FOR LATE 20TH CENTURY WELTSCHMERZ??

BUZBY, ARE YOU TAPING THIS?

LEAVE ME ALONE MUM!

BUZBY

MAKE SURE YOU BRING THE TROTSKYISTS, SEAMUS

HELLO, KARLA...

I'M JUST A TWITTERING EXCRESCENCE! MY LIFE IS MEANINGLESS!

HOW WOULD YOU LIKE TO BE SMOGGLED OUT OF CONTRY YIN WHEEL-BARROW?

BUZBY

IF...

...I NEED HARDLY STRESS THE **GRAVITY** OF THE SITUATION CHIEF CONSTABLE....

..THE **ENEMY** HAVE **ABDUCTED** THIS **BIRD**, AND IF BY ANY CHANCE HE SHOULD **SING**, WE COULD **ALL** FIND OURSELVES IN **QUEER STREET!**

YOU CAN **COUNT** ON **US**, MA'AM!

...MY **WOODENTOPS** WILL BE **DOWN** ON THESE **HOMOSEXUALS** LIKE A **TON** OF **BRICKS!** WE'LL STAKE OUT EVERY **PUBLIC CONVENIENCE** BETWEEN **HERE** AND JOHN O'GROATS WITHIN THE **HOUR!**

I THINK YOU MAY HAVE **MISTAKEN** MY **DRIFT**, CHIEF CONSTABLE — —IN THIS INSTANCE WE'RE AFTER **BIRD LOVERS**, NOT...

...EVERY DUCK POND, EVERY **CHICKEN** RUN, EVERY **PIGEON** COOP, EVERY **ORNITHOLOGIST CELL!!**...

© Steve Bell 1982.

IF...

THE STORY SO FAR: **PYOTR LEFLEGIN** IS SMUGGLING THE DEFECTING **BUZBY** OUT OF THE COUNTRY IN A STOLEN **WHEELBARROW**...... **POLICE** ARE ON THE LOOKOUT FOR **BIRD SYMPATHISERS**.....

SING!

OI! FUNNY FACE!!! WHAT YOU GOT IN THAT WHEELBARROW?

© Steve Bell

I YAM REPORTER FOR **'SUN'** NEWSPAPER — YIS **NORMAL** PROCEDURE — I DON'T USE **NOTEBOOK**—

I USE **WHEELBARROW** FULL OF OLD **LAVATORY** PAPER...

PASS FRIEND

IF... AT LAST IT CAN BE TOLD: THE **TRUE STORY** BEHIND ONE OF THE **GREATEST DISAPPEARING TROUSER MYSTERIES** OF MODERN TIMES!!

THE NONENTITY

MANCHESTER, NOVEMBER 1982

GEOFFREY?!

© STEVE BELL 1982

GEOFFREY — I ADMIRE THE **FORTHRIGHT** WAY YOU **KICKED THAT BEGGAR** BUT I WONDER, WAS IT **ENTIRELY POLITIC** TO DO IT IN **PUBLIC** IN WHAT MAY BE THE **RUN UP TO A GENERAL ELECTION**??

WHAT ARE YOU TALKING ABOUT, MARGARET?

315

...NOW YOU'RE **TAP DANCING**!

NONSENSE MAG — I CAN'T TAP DA...**GOOD GRIEF**!!

SNIKKETY SNAK-A-SNAK-A-SNIKETY..

IF... ...I CAN'T **UNDERSTAND** IT, MAG! — EVERY TIME I SEE AN **OLD AGE PENSIONER,** MY **LEGS** SEEM TO TAKE ON A **LIFE** OF THEIR **OWN!**

BOOT!

IT'S FRANKLY **DISTURBING!**

YOU YOUNG DEVIL — YOU JUST **POGOED** ON ME **CORNS**!!

BOING! MOAN

© STEVE BELL 1982

...ANOTHER THING — MY **LEGS** START **TAP DANCING** ENTIRELY **SPONTANEOUSLY**...

SNIKKETY SNAK

SNAT

...WHENEVER I GO PAST A **BANK**!!

BANK

SPPING

IF...

I THINK THE ATTACK IS PASSING, MAG — I'M ACTUALLY PUTTING MY HAND INTO MY POCKET FOR THAT BEGGAR CHAP...

SIX ECONOMIC UNITS OF SUPPORT

HERE YOU ARE.... ...TRY NOT TO SPEND IT ALL AT ONCE!..

FLIP

GOD BLESS YOU SIR

© Steve Bell 1982

317

WHERE DID YOU GET THOSE TROUSERS GEOFFREY??

CLAW

THE EAST IS RED

IF...

© STEVE BELL 1982

HELP! QUICK!! SEND AN AMBULANCE!!

I'M AFRAID I CAN'T STOP MYSELF!

318.

I WAS STANDING IN A QUEUE AT THE D.H.S.S., WHEN THIS MANIAC STARTS TRYING TO STRANGLE ME WITH HIS LEGS!

I'M NOT A MANIAC YOU KNOW..

...MAKE SURE YOU BRING A HUMANE KILLER!!

I'M ...CHANCELLOR OF THE EXCHEQUER!

?

THE REST IS HISTORY...

Ronald Reagan

**Born Grantham, Illinois
1826**

Renowned as the youthful
star of such epics as
'Bathtime for Bumbo' and
'Paint Your Hair On!',
Ronald Reagan subsequently
became front man for a
group of Californian
businessmen with political
ambitions, calling
themselves 'The Winged
Psychos of Destiny to Stomp
Out Godless Pink Subversion
Today League', now known
more succinctly as the
'Kitchen Cabinet'.

Reagan's administration
has been most notable for
the calibre of his advisers,
the foremost among these
being William P. Clark and
Francis the Talking Mule.
His interests include getting
good shut-eye and eating
regular.

71

IF...

CHIEF CONSTABLE—
—COULD YOU TELL US WHAT
THE NEW POLICE POWERS
ACT WILL MEAN FOR
YOUR FORCE?

CHIEF CONSTABLE
'BADGER' COURAGE

THE BASIC FUNCTION OF
THIS ACT IS SIMPLY ONE
OF CLARIFICATION.

~SLEEK~

© STEVE BELL 1982 - 327

TO CLARIFY
WHAT EXACTLY,
CHIEF CONSTABLE??

CHIEF CONSTABLE
'BADGER' COURAGE

THAT HE CAN DO EXACTLY
WHAT HE LIKES, WHEN HE
LIKES, WHERE HE LIKES,
TO WHOEVER HE LIKES!

I LIKE
MONKEYS,
JOHN

CHIEF CONSTABLE
'BADGER' COURAGE

~THANKS TO JIM WARNER~

IF...

© STEVE BELL 1982

THE NEW ACT WILL
CLARIFY CERTAIN
HITHERTO PROBLEMATIC
AREAS OF POLICE PRACTICE...

32.8

...BY REMOVING THE RAGBAG
OF CONFUSED 'AD HOC' GUIDE-
LINES LIKE J.R. (JUDGES RULES)
S.A.S. (STOP AND SEARCH) SUS
U.A.C.T.B.J. (UNNECESSARY
AND COSTLY TRIAL BY JURY).....

...AND REPLACE THEM WITH
ONE UNIFIED PRINCIPLE
WHICH POLICE AND PUBLIC
ALIKE CAN FULLY COMP-
-REHEND. WE CALL IT:
N.A.I.D.L.Y.F.U.A.T.W.O.I.K.Y.H.I.J.
OR NAIDLYF FOR SHORT.

NAIDLYF??

NO ARGUMENT, I DON'T LIKE YOUR
FACE-UP AGAINST THAT WALL OR I'LL
KICK YOUR HEAD
IN, JOHN!

IF... BUT OF COURSE, THE **REAL REASON** WE IN THE POLICEFORCE **NEED** THESE **EXTRA POWERS**...

...IS TO ENABLE US TO CATCH THE **REAL VILLAINS** - THE **BIG BOYS**, THE **PROFESSIONAL WRONGDOERS** - TO PREVENT **THESE** PEOPLE...

...FROM WRIGGLING THROUGH **LOOPHOLES** IN THE **LAW** WITH THE AID OF UNSCRUPULOUS **BRIEFS**. **NOW** WE'VE GOT A **REAL CHANCE** OF PICKING THESE TYPES UP ON THE **STREET** - AND ONCE NICKED, REST ASSURED THEY'LL **STAY NICKED**!

© STEVE BELL 1982 - 329.

PARDON ME, BUT I HAVE **REASON** TO **BELIEVE** THAT THERE IS A **ONE** IN **FIFTY SIX MILLION** CHANCE THAT **YOU** MAY BE **LORD LUCAN**!

IF... 330 ALWAYS REMEMBER, MR. **BLOCKHEAD**, THAT **OUT HERE** ON THE **STREET** IS WHERE THE **ACT** IS GOING TO MAKE A **BIG DIFFERENCE**...

...WITH INCREASED TRAINING AND RESPONSIBILITY, **TOMORROW'S POLICEPERSON** WILL BE VERY DIFFERENT FROM THE **TRUNCHEONED IGNORAMUS** OF YESTERYEAR.

...HE OR SHE WILL BE **ARTICULATE** WELL-VERSED IN **LAW**, FAMILIAR WITH THE MOST **SOPHISTICATED COMPUTER SYSTEMS** AND **THIEF-TAKING TECHNOLOGY** - BY NO MEANS A **SQUARE-BASHING AUTOMATON**!

SHINE YOUR SHOES, SIR?

NO... JUST **BUFF** UP THE **BACK** OF ME **HEAD**, JOHN!

© STEVE BELL 1982

75

IF... I SAY AGAIN, COMRADE, THAT UNLESS A **VIGOROUS** AND **COMMITTED TURKEY VANGUARD** IS PREPARED TO **SELFLESSLY DIRECT** THE **LEGITIMATE** AND **INEXORABLE** ASPIRATIONS OF THE **BROAD MASS** OF THE **TURKEY MOVEMENT**, THEN I **FORESEE** A SITUATION WHERE....

TURKEY TROT!!

KILL!

© STEVE BELL 1982

TIME WAS WHEN YOU WOULD HAVE BEEN OUT ON YOUR EAR BEFORE YOU WERE EVEN HATCHED, YOU TROT BASTARD!!

DON'T WORRY— WE'VE GOT AN ANSWER FOR YOUR KIND NOW!...

333

HOW LONG HAVE YOU BEEN A TURKEY?

ALL MY LIFE.

ARE YOU OR HAVE YOU EVER BEEN A DUCK?

NO.

WHAT IS THE TURKEY CODE?

GOBBLE GOBBLE GOBBLE.

TURKEY REGISTER

IF... RIGHT... **PUSH OFF!**— —YOU'RE HEREBY **EXPELLED** FROM THE TURKEY MOVEMENT....

WHO SAYS?? WHAT FOR???

TURKEY REGISTER

I GAVE ALL THE **RIGHT ANSWERS** TO YOUR QUESTIONS— WHAT HAVE I DONE WRONG??

YOU'RE AN ANTI DEMOCRATIC ELEMENT, YOU SCUM!

334

ANTIDEMOCRATIC??? WHAT POSSIBLE **GROUNDS**....

ALL THOSE WHO AGREE WITH THE PROPOSITION THAT THIS BIRD IS ANTIDEMOCRATIC PLEASE **RAISE THEIR WINGS**... ...CARRIED UNANIMOUSLY!!

© STEVE BELL 1982

DON'T **I** GET A VOTE?

YOU DON'T GET ONE BECAUSE YOU'RE ANTIDEMOCRATIC

IF... THIS 'OLE BEEZNESS DEESRURPT MA CRÉATIVITÉ AND MAKE ME VAIR' DEPRESSED!! I RETURN TO MA BED!!

QUOI? MOI?

TING-A-LING -A-LING!

SO!! WOOMAN — YOU 'AVE THE AUDACITÉ TO REENG ME URP!? — 'OW DARE YOU LEAVE MOI FOR SOME STUPIDE 'PEACE CAMP'!!

QUOI? M

SO YOU ARE WORRIED ABOUT THE BURMB? POUF!! ALWAYS THERE WILL BE THE BURMB!! WHAT GOOD WILL A BURNCH OF CREZZY WEEMEN DO?? MY ART IS MEUR REAL AND MEUR IMPORTANTE THAN THESE CREZZY WEEMEN!!

341

...'OW DARE YOU CALL ME A OUANQUÈRE!

© Steve Bell 1982

IF... WOOMAN! — WHAT MAKES YOU THINK YOU CAN SUDDENLY GET REED OF THE BURMB??

QUOI? MOI? HA!

© Steve Bell 1982

ALWAYS THERE WILL BE THE BURMB!! WHAT YOU CREZZY WEEMEN ARE DOING IS FUTILE* YOU ARE PLAYING THE BOURGEOIS MINDGAMES!! DON' EXPECT TO COME CRURLING BACK 'ERE WHEN YOU GET BEURRED!!

*pron: FOOTEEL

SO? IT'S YOUR FLAT?! — — I DON' GIVE A MEURNKEYS! I CAN LIVE MA LIFE WEEZOUT WEEMEN! WHAT ARE YOU FOR MOI EXCEPT THE MERE DISTRACTION??!

I THINK I GO DOWN THE PEURB

QUOI? MOI? HA!

342

81

82

"Lord" Rupert Dingo
Born Grantham, New South Wales 1926

Rupert Dingo first came to prominence as proprietor and editor of 'The Wombat', "The All-Australian newspaper that really digs the dirt". From this base he developed an empire that has spread to include newspapers and TV channels right across the globe, and which includes in this country alone, the 'Mule' group, the 'Stoat' group, and the jewel in his crown, the world's oldest giveaway smear sheet 'The Thunderbox'. His interests include bushwalking by proxy and the aristocracy.

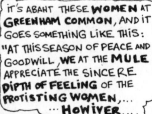

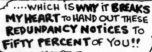

85

93

94

Chief Constable Gerald 'Badger' Courage

Born Grantham Police Station 1926

'Badger' Courage joined the Army at the age of five and rose to the rank of Private by the outbreak of the Second World War. He was mentioned in despatches twice due to his outstanding ability to polish up the back of his head.

Demobilised in 1946, he spent a brief interlude as a successful armed robber, but became increasingly depressed out of uniform, and joined the Police force in 1948. His interests include monkeys and religion.

IF... "BLUDGEON'S THE NAME — RICK BLUDGEON — AGENT FOR MI6 AND THE FREEWORLD® DOUBLE GLAZING CORP.....

...CHAIN-SMOKER, LIFE-TAKER.....ON SECONDMENT TO THE D.H.S.S. PRESENT ASSIGNMENT —

—TO GET DIRT ON A COHABITATION SUSPECT IN PECKHAM. THERE WAS SOMETHING DIRTY GOING ON IN THERE.

© Steve Bell 1983—

THIS IS A DIRTY WORLD AND I'M A DIRTY GUY."

3/6/5

IF... "MY SUSPECT WAS MALE, CAUCASIAN, 6 FEET, 200 POUNDS, WITH A FACE LIKE AN AUTOMOBILE WRECK.....

..MY INFORMATION SAID HE WAS LIVING OFF A FEMALE AND USING STATE HANDOUTS TO BUY COLOUR TEEVEES. THE FEMALE WAS THERE ALL RIGHT, AND THEY WERE GETTING FRIENDLY...

THEN SOMETHING CAUGHT MY EYE, AND I KNEW I HAD THE CREEP. NOT ONLY WAS I GOING TO GET THIS GUY A HEAVY FINE AND SAVE THE STATE UP TO £25 A WEEK....

...HE WAS GOING TO GO DOWN FOR HARBOURING A KNOWN TERRORIST!!! "

OH SOLE MIO-O-O!

3/6/6

© Steve Bell 1983

96

IF... "IT WASN'T JUST **ANY** FED, IT WAS A **BIG FED.** I KNEW THEY WERE **SERIOUS.** THIS GUY WAS **NO SLOUCH**......

...WE MOVED TO THE **STAKE--OUT.** THEY'D BROUGHT UP THE **HEAVY STUFF**.......

THOSE **CREEPS** DIDN'T **STAND A CHANCE.** "

I GOT **MEDALS,** JOHN...

TIN HAT, JOHN?

PENGUIN!! WE KNOW YOU'RE IN **THERE!!!**

I KNOW I'M IN HERE **TOO!!** LET'S HAVE A **SHOUTING MATCH!!!**

IF... "THEY GAVE UP **WITHOUT A FIGHT. IT WAS TOUGH.** I COULDA **USED** A **SHOOT-OUT** RIGHT THEN. BUT I'M A **PRO. EMOTIONAL INVOLVEMENT'S** NOT MY BRAND OF **HAMBURGER**...

...SOMETIMES, THOUGH, IT'S **HARD.** THESE **CREEPS**'LL PUSH YOU TO THE **LIMIT**........

THE **FEMALE** SOUNDED **FOREIGN.** I KNEW HOW TO **HANDLE** THE SITUATION....." "

HELLO RATFACE!

370

NOBODY CALLS ME **RATFACE** YOU **STINKIN' PINKO PENGUIN PUNK!!** I'M GONNA PUMP YOU FULLA......

EASY JOHN!

RELAXEZ CHERIE. MAYBE WE CAN WORK SOMETHING OUT....

KEEPLING! PINGOUIN!! WHERE YOU TAKE THEM?

DID ANYBODY EVAIR TELL YOU THAT YOU 'AVE THE **FACE** JUSTE LIKE THE **BEELGE RAT?**

NNNGK!

© Steve Bell 1983

98

102

IF... STILL NO SIGN OF MA **WOOMAN**, THOUGH A LITTLE OISEAU TELL ME SHE IS NOW INVEULVED WITH A **MATELOT**..... ....WHAT IS **THIS**??.... ....ANOTHER **NEURT**???

ONCE WE 'AD SOMETHING VAIR' **BIG**, VAIR' **IMPORTANTE** TOGETHAIR. NOW IT IS REDUCED TO **KRYPTIQUE NEURTS** ONCE IN A **BLEU MOON**. IT MAKE ME FAIRLY UN'APPY.

WHAT DOES SHE SAY? SHE WANT ME TO **LOOK** AFTER **TWO** OF 'ER FRIENDS FOR A SHORT WHILE. **PAH!** I THINK SHE TRY AND **MAKE THE MEURNKEY OUT OF MOI** IN MA' **OWN 'OME!!**

© Steve Bell 1983 --- 379.

YOU **COULD** SAY THAT, MATEY!...

QUOI?

IF... © Steve Bell 1983 ---

SO, SHE 'AS **LUMBAIRED** ME WITH A **MEURNKEY**, AND **YOU** — I RECOGNISE **YOU**! — YOU ARE THE **PINGOUIN** FROM **DOWNSTAIRS**, BUT YOU ARE WEARING THE **WIG!!**

SPOT ON, MATEY!!

WHY DON'T YOU **GO DOWNSTAIRS** AND LEAVE MOI ALONE, HEIN?

BECAUSE OF THE **OLD BILL**, MATEY! THERE'S **WALL TO WALL BOYS IN BLUE** DOWN THERE, Y'KNOW....

I WISH TO REMAIN **INCOGNITO**, AS THEY SAY. AND MY FRIEND THE **PRIMATE** HERE IS A **KEY WITNESS** IN A FORTHCOMING **CORRUPTION TRIAL** WHO MUST BE PROTECTED AT ALL COSTS!!

THIS IS SO MUCH **CREZZY NONSENSE** — LET ME **LOOK**!

380.

HOLD IT RIGHT THERE!!

EARLY SMIRK!! THE **OUTRAGEOUS ARTISTES** IN **BLEU** ARE STAGING SOME KIND OF '**APPENING!!** I AM **WILDLY EXCITED!!**

I THINK WE'RE ONTO SOMETHING SARGE!

103

The Monkey
Born Grantham Zoo, Lincs
1926

The Monkey spent his formative years as an associate of violent criminals in London's East End. Presented, by way of a joke, as a bribe to the then simple Police Constable 'Badger' Courage, the Monkey soon became Badger's indispensable accomplice. As their relationship blossomed, so did Badger's career in the force. By virtue of his ready intelligence and his contacts in the underworld, the Monkey helped to bring numerous villains to book, including most of Badger's superior officers.

The Monkey's life changed abruptly when he met the Penguin, who turned him on to animal rights, amongst other things. His interests include bananas and betting on the dogs.

IF... "BLUDGEON'S THE NAME — RICK BLUDGEON — LICENCED TO KILL, MAIM AND ASK IMPERTINENT QUESTIONS. CURRENTLY ON SECONDMENT TO THE D.H.S.S....

CURRENT ASSIGNMENT — THE KIPLING FILE. I NEEDED TO **NAIL** THAT GUY, BUT THE CASE HAD **TURNED SOUR**..........

...MY PRINCIPAL **ALLY**, A **BIG FED** NAME OF **COURAGE**, HAD BEEN THROWN IN THE **SLAMMER** ON ACCOUNT OF SOME TWO-TIMING **CREEP** OF A **MONKEY** GRASSING ON HIM....

YOU'VE GOTTA GET ME OUT OF HERE, BLUDGEON!

I'M DOING WHAT I CAN!

...SOMEHOW I HAD TO **CLEAR** THE **BIG FED'S** NAME. IT WASN'T GOING TO BE **EASY.** "

LISTEN, FED — I KNOW A REAL MEAN LAWYER — HE'S, SHALL WE SAY 'AMENABLE TO PECUNIARY CONSIDERATIONS'

LISTEN, SUNBEAM — WITH WHAT THAT MONKEY'S GOT ON ME, I NEED MORE THAN A BENT BRIEF! — I NEED A **BENT JUDGE**, KNOW WHAT I MEAN?

IF... "THE **BIG FED** HAD SET MY MIND WORKING. HIS **CASE** CAME UP THAT WEEK, AND IF I COULD SOMEHOW "**GET TO**" THE **JUDGE**, THEN **MAYBE**, JUST MAYBE I COULD **SWING** SOMETHING....

...BUT **HOW?** THESE **JUDGE** GUYS WERE WAY ABOVE MY REGULAR **RANGE** OF **CONTACTS**.... ...RUMOUR HAD IT THAT **THIS** PARTICULAR JUDGE WAS **CARRIED AROUND IN A CHAIR**.......

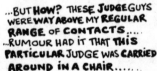

...HOW THE **HELL** COULD I "GET TO" A GUY WHO'S CARRIED AROUND IN A CHAIR?? THEN IT **HIT** ME LIKE A **WESTBOUND TRAIN**!!..

WAHOOO!

SNAP!

...THE HAND THAT **CARRIES** THE CHAIR ROCKS THE JUDGE! "

THIS COULD BE MY **BIG BREAK**!!

YELLOW PAGES

CHAIR CARRYING CONSULTANCIES

© Steve Bell 1983 — 384 ..

IF... "THE JUDGE I WAS AFTER USED FLUNKEYS FROM AN UPTOWN FLUNKEY AGENCY TO CARRY HIM AROUND IN A... CHAIR..........

...PHYLLIS, THE OWNER, TOOK ME ON, NO QUESTIONS ASKED...

LEMME SEE YOUR LEGS!

...THE UNIFORM LOOKED WELL ON ME, THOUGH I DO SAY SO MYSELF, THE WIG, HOWEVER, WAS THREE SIZES TOO LARGE.....

...FORTUNATELY THERE WAS JUST ROOM TO PACK MY ROD IN THERE..... "

© Steve Bell 1983

IF... "THE CHAIR WAS A NEAT CONTRAPTION.....

...BUT THERE WAS SOMETHING ODD ABOUT THE JUDGE...

TO THE TEMPLE OF RA, DOGS!

SNAK

...MY PLAN WAS SIMPLE— PRODUCE THE GUN FROM UNDER MY WIG AND START NEGOTIATIONS. IF HE DIDN'T SEE THINGS MY WAY, I'D THREATEN TO BLOW HIS JAWBONE AWAY.

© Steve Bell 1983   - 386 -

...BUT IT WAS GOING TO BE DIFFICULT. THIS GUY WAS A CANDIDATE FOR THE FUNNY FARM..... "

BY ISIS!! WHY DO YOU DROP ASH ON THE ROBE OF TUTANKHAMEN SLAVE WITH THE VISAGE OF A RAT?

109

IF... ACE JOURNALIST BARRY BLOCKHEAD, HAVING CHANGED PLACES WITH A DISSIDENT LACKEY HAS INFILTRATED THE PALACE...

LACKEY!! BRING ME SOME BUTTERED TOAST AND A HORSEWHIP!!

© Steve Bell 1983

LACKEY!! BRING ME MY BONDAGE TRIZERS!

LACKEY!

?

LACKEY!? WHAT'S THE MATTER WITH YOU??

LOOK SHARP THERE, LACKEY!

I'M NOT HERE! I'M NOT HERE!!

397

DON'T JUST STAND THERE GIBBERING, LACKEY!!

HAS THIS LACKEY BEEN POSITIVELY VETTED??

OH NO! OH NO!!

IF... BARRY BLOCKHEAD IS INSIDE THE PALACE POSING AS A LACKEY...

FALL AHT FOR POSITIVE VETTING PROCEDURES, THAT LACKEY THERE!!

OH NO! TELL ME IT ISN'T TRUE!

POSITIVE VETTING BY NUMBAHS ...ONE.... ARE YOU NOW OR HAVE YOU EVAH BEEN A PINKO??

ERRM.... NO WAY

...TWO... ARE YOU NOW, OR HAVE YOU EVAH BEEN A POOFTAH??

..ER.... ABSOLUTELY NO WAY SIR!

© Steve Bell 1983 — 398.

CARRY ON, THAT LACKEY....

HELLO?? NEWSDESK?? PUT ME THROUGH TO HARRY HARDNOSE, PLEASE....

© Steve Bell 1983

HARRY?? —I'VE GOT A HOT STORY HERE... "PRINCESS OF WALES ACCIDENTALLY MACHINE-GUNS MATING DUCKS ON PALACE LAKE!!!"

WHAT DO YOU MEAN 'IT'S NO GOOD'??! IT'S GOT ANIMALS, SEX, VIOLENCE, ROYALTY —WHAT MORE DO YOU WANT??

YOU WANT SOMETHING THE PUNTERS CAN IDENTIFY WITH? GORDON BENNETT!

ALRIGHT...WHAT ABOUT THIS... "QUEEN USED OWN LEGS TO WALK DOWNSTAIRS BOMBSHELL" ...OR HOW ABOUT... "DUKE TOOK CLOTHES OFF TO GET IN BATH SENSATION"

399.

HOW ABOUT... "PRINCE DEALS WITH SCALP ITCH IN AMUSINGLY UNEXPECTED FASHION — 'HE JUST SAT THERE AND SCRATCHED IT!' —REMARKED AWESTRUCK AIDE..."

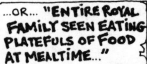

...OR... "ENTIRE ROYAL FAMILY SEEN EATING PLATEFULS OF FOOD AT MEALTIME..." ...LISTEN HARRY, WHAT AM I SUPPOSED TO BE DOING HERE? YOU REALISE THAT IF I MAKE ONE FALSE MOVE I STAND TO GET BANGED UP IN BROADMOOR INDEFINITELY?!

HARRY, WHY ARE THE INTIMATE ACTIVITIES OF THIS FRANKLY UNDISTINGUISHED GROUP OF INDIVIDUALS SO IMPORTANT TO YOU?? WHY ARE YOU GOING TO SUCH LENGTHS OF SORDID SUBTERFUGE. WHAT MANIA IS DRIVING YOU ON??

...YOU WANT A KNIGHTHOOD AND LORD DINGO WANTS A DUKEDOM? I SEE——

Steve Bell 1983

400.

115

IF... 403.

MR CLEAN'S GONE — —YOU CAN **SPEAK FREELY** NOW, NED...

BLEEDIN' WIMPISH CHINESE LIBERALS!

© Steve Bell 1983

CHINESE LIBERALS? WHAT ARE YOU ON ABOUT, NED?

THEY'RE VERY WISHEE WASHEE, HARRY! SNUK SNUK..

TO BE **SERIOUS**, THOUGH — —IT'S **POLICIES** THAT **COUNT**, AND **WE** SAY: **SMASH THE UNIONS!** MORE **POWERS** FOR THE **POLICE! BIGGER** AND MORE **SENSIBLE BOMBS!** MORE **PRIVATISATION!!** ABOLISH **TROTSKYIST LESBIANS IN WOOLLY HATS!**

...AND THAT'S WHY **WE** IN THE **SDP** ARE THE **ONLY CREDIBLE OPPOSITION** TO THE **CONSERVATIVE PARTY!!**

WIGHT ON!

IF...

© Steve Bell 1983

...BESIDES, **WE** IN THE **SDP** HAVE GOT AN **ASSET** THAT **NONE** OF THE **OTHERS** CAN **HOPE** TO **APPROACH!**...

..NO, I'M NOT TALKING ABOUT **SHIRL THE PEARL, DOCTOR DEATH** OR **WILD BILL** ...AND I'M **CERTAINLY NOT** TALKING ABOUT **YOU, WOY!**

404

SHAME!

.. I'M TALKING ABOUT THE **NEWT** ......THE LATEST POLL SHOWS **CONCLUSIVELY** THAT HE'S **MORE POPULAR** THAN STEEL, THATCHER, FOOT, E.T., KEN + DEIRDRE, THE POPE AND **CHAMPION THE WONDER HORSE** COMBINED!!

...AND WHAT'S MORE HE'S PROMISED TO MAKE A **STATEMENT** ON STRATEGY **RIGHT NOW!**

VOTE LABOUR

117

Barry Blockhead
Born Grantham, Lincs 1926

'The Man with a Nose for What Mr & Mrs Average-Punter Want to Read About' entered journalism after an unsuccessful career as a male model. His outstanding lack of scruple was soon spotted by Harry Hardnose, and he rapidly became one of the Mule's star reporters, covering such important stories as the 'Dead Red's Bed Found in Shed Horror' and the 'Dog Show Sex Ring Scandal'.

However, a sharp blow to the head sustained during the Falklands conflict did something to re-awaken his dormant sense of moral discrimination, if only temporarily. He now works for BBC News. His interests include raincoats, trilbies and bizarre sex.

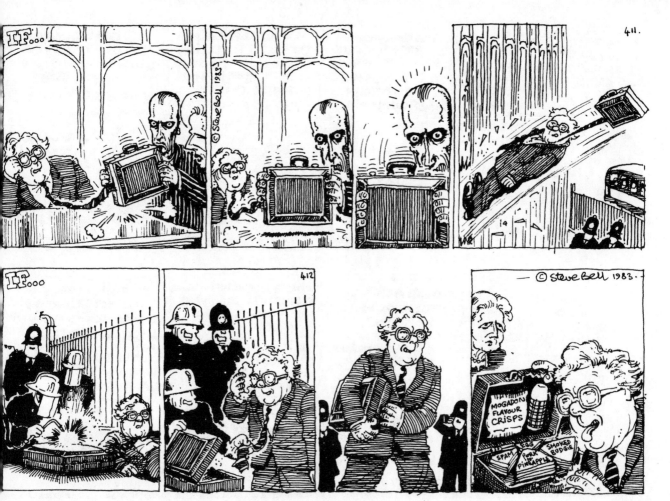

121

IF... © Steve Bell - 1983

I'M **FED UP** WITH THE 'MORNING MULE', HARRY!

TURN IT UP, BAZ — I WANT YOU TO GET INSIDE THIS HORSE SUIT AND **FIND SHERGAR!**

412

I'M **SERIOUS**, HARRY I'M **TIRED** OF WRITING **LIES, SMEARS** AND **TRASH** TO PLEASE SOME **ANTIPO DEAN MEGALOMANIAC!**

YOU DON'T **BELIEVE** ME, **DO YOU**? I'M **TELLING** YOU NOW — I'M **FINISHED** WITH THIS **BASTION** OF **BIGOTRY**, THIS **RANCID RAG!!**

IT'S **GOODBYE**, HARDNOSE — I'M GETTING SOME **BALANCE** INTO MY LIFE — I'VE GOT A JOB AT THE **B.B.C!!!**

NYAHAHHA HA HAHAHAAA!!

IF...   414

ER...EXCUSE ME... IS THIS THE INDUCTION COURSE FOR **BBC** NEWS REPORTERS??

YES AND NO...

© Steve Bell 1983 —

I'M **BARRY BLOCKHEAD**, FORMERLY OF THE 'MULE', HOW DO YOU DO??

AND IT'S GOODMORNING FROM ME, **ROGER SNOYD**... ...AND FROM ME, **TESSA RAMPART**...

...AND **TODAY** WE'RE LOOKING AT **HAIRCUTS**. JUST **WHAT** MAKES PEOPLE HAVE **HAIRCUTS??**...

NOW TELL US, MR. BLOCKHEAD, HOW WOULD YOU **EXPLAIN** YOUR **HAIRCUT??**

I..I..ER..

...BECAUSE, **SURELY**, YOU'RE **NOT TRYING** TO **SUGGEST** TO US THAT YOU HAVE A **BALANCED** HAIRCUT?

...WELL, THAT'S ABOUT **ALL WE'VE** GOT TIME FOR NOW...

IF... — © Steve Bell 1983 —

BBC NEWS REPORTERS INDUCTION COURSE

GOOD MORNING

IN ANY **BROADCAST MEDIUM**, THE **QUALITY** AND **TONE** OF **ONE'S** VOICE IS OF THE **UTMOST IMPORTANCE!**...

IN **NEWS** INTERVIEWS, WE AT THE **BBC** AIM FOR A **DISTINCTIVE SOUND QUALITY** IN **ALL** OUR QUESTIONING — —AS OUR **FIRST GUEST** IS HERE TO **DEMONSTRATE**.

45.

QUACK QUACK QUAAACK QUACK QUACKQUACK!

BBC NEWS RE INDUCTION

IF... © Steve Bell 1983

QUACK QUACK QUACK QUAAACK NYAAA QUACK QUACKQUACK...

BBC NEWS INDUCTION COURSE

NYAA QUACK!

VERY GOOD, MR. SNOYD — PERHAPS YOU COULD HAVE CURLED YOUR LIP A **FRACTION** MORE...... BUT I DON'T WISH TO **CARP**.....

NOW WE'VE GOT THE **OVERALL SOUND QUALITY** ABOUT RIGHT, WE MOVE ONTO **NEWSREADING PROPER**...... OK MISS RAMPART?

AHEM...

46.

QUACK QUACK SCARGILL QUACK QUACK MILITANT QUACK KING ARTHUR QUACK QUACK SO-CALLED QUACK SCARGILL FACTOR QUACK QUACK FAILURE QUACK QUESTION MARK QUACK QUACK LEADERSHIP

IF... THAT'S IT! — REALLY **SPIT** THOSE WORDS OUT, MR. **BLOCKHEAD**!

BBC NEWS INDUCTION COURSE

SCARGILL PTUI PTUI! SCARGILL! SCARRGILLPTUI!

MOVING ON NOW TO NEWS ITEMS ABOUT THE PRIME MINISTER... ...MR. **BLOCKHEAD**, PERHAPS IF YOU COULD **EXHIBIT RESPECT** IN YOUR READING?

"THERE IS SAID TO BE ANGER AT DOWNINGSTREET..."

NO, THAT WAS **QUITE HOPELESS** BLOCKHEAD — CONSIDER YOURSELF **DISMISSED**!! ....AND BY THE WAY — YOUR **FLIES** ARE **UNDONE**! BEFORE YOU **GO**, WOULD YOU MIND **READING IT OUT ONE MORE TIME**?

"THERE IS SAID TO BE ANGER AT DOWNING ST..."

EXCELLENT! — THAT'S EXACTLY THE DEGREE OF **AWESTRUCK SHEEPISHNESS** I WANTED!

©Steve Bell 1983

IF... OK, BLOCKHEAD — **OUT** YOU GO!! THIS IS A **FIELD TEST**! FROM THAT MILLING CROWD I WANT YOU TO PICK OUT AND QUESTION A **MILITANT TROUBLE MAKER**!!

PARDON ME, SIR.... ...MADAM...EXCUSE ME... ...I'D LIKE TO ASK..... ...JUST **ONE MOMENT**.! — GOD, THEY **ALL** LOOK THE **SAME**!

YOU THERE IN THE **WOOLLY HAT** — YOU LOOK LIKE A **MILITANT**..... WHAT HAVE **YOU** GOT TO SAY FOR YOURSELF?

©Steve Bell 1983

QUACK QUACK QUAC DESTROY PANORAMA QUACK QUACK QUAC BRING BACK WOODENTOP QUACK QUACK QUAC PHITHHHARRRRPP!

124

IF... RONNEEEE!! CHOW TIME!!

YOWSA!

OH BOY OH BOY! — —BOTULO-BURGER WITH CHOCOLATE SAUCE, CHERRY PIE AND MAYONNAISE! YUMMY NIMMYNUMKINS!!

DON'T MAKE YOURSELF SICK NOW, HONEY!

© Steve Bell 1983

425.

I HAD A DREAM JUST NOW, NANCY (GBWORRRP!)

GOSH, RON YOU'RE SUCH AN IDEALIST!

I DREAMT THAT THE SOVIETS WERE HAMBURGERS AND I WAS A MICRO--WAVE OVEN!!

IF... I'M GETTING UP UP UP!!! A BRAND NEW DAY IS DAWNIN!!

© Steve Bell 1983

I'M PUTTIN' ON A NEW HAT AND I'VE GOT A NEW MESSAGE TO GIVE THE WORLD!

MY NEW HAT HAS GOT A PERSONALISED DEATH RAY!

ZAP!

NOW I CAN JUST LAUGH AT ASSASSINATION ATTEMPTS!

MY FRIENDS — I DREAM OF A WORLD WHERE EVERY AMERICAN SHALL HAVE HIS OWN PERSONALISED DEATH RAY!

426.

IF... CASPAR WEINBURGER, YOU OL' SON OF A GUN! PUT IT THERE, PAL!!

WE GOT'EM ON THE RUN, CASPAR!!

DAM'RIGHT RON!!

© Steve Bell —1983— 427.

ZAP!

HELL, CASPAR! MY PERSONALISED DEATH RAY NEARLY BLEW YOUR HEAD OFF BY ACCIDENT!

THAT WOULD HAVE BEEN A MAJOR SETBACK FOR THE WESTERN WORLD, RON!

IF... CASPAR.... I HAD A GREAT DEFENSE IDEA THE OTHER NIGHT, AND I WANNA KNOW IF IT'S ECONOMICALLY VIABLE.

SURE IT IS, RON- WHAT IS IT??

MICROWAVE

KLIK

© Steve Bell 1983—

I WANT YOU TO IMAGINE THE SOVIET UNION AS A GIANT CHEESEBURGER!

I CAN SEE IT, RON, I CAN SEE IT!!

..NOW I WANT YOU TO VISUALISE A STRING OF GIANT SATELLITES READY TO BEAM MICROWAVE ENERGY ONTO THAT CHEESEBURGER AT THE FLICK OF A SWITCH!

I'M EXPERIENCING IT, RON! I'M EXPERIENCING IT IN MY HEAD!!

428.

NOW ASK YOURSELF-- IF YOU WERE THAT CHEESEBURGER WOULD YOU DARE STEP OUT OF LINE?

NO WAY RON!!

127

F...

TARZAN WILL RETURN!

433

TARZAN WILL MOBILISE SILENT JUNGLE MAJORITY....

TARZAN WILL CATCH POPULAR IMAGINATION AND BUILD MASS MOVEMENT!!

HMMM.... PERHAPS WE NEED SNAPPIER TITLE.

LADIES WITH FUR COATS, PLACES IN BUNKERS AND SHARES IN THE DEFENCE INDUSTRY FOR CRUISE AND TRIDENT

IF...

TODAY SEE TARZAN SCORE MAJOR PROPAGANDA COUP!!

"LADIES WITH BUNKERS FOR CRUISE AND TRIDENT" STAGE MASS DEMONSTRATION...

...LINKING HANDS BETWEEN HARRODS AND THE OTHER SIDE OF THE ROAD!

© Steve Bell 1983

ARE WE ALLOWED TO USE SERVANTS?

Harrods

434

129

IF...

TARZAN INSPECT BUNKER CONSTRUCTION SITE....

SEE TARZAN..... MIGHTY BUNKER IS BIG AND BROAD AS HOLLOW MOUNTAIN!

435.

...INSIDE IS GREAT WHITE BIRD, SWIFTER AND DEADLIER THAN THE STOOPING FALCON...

...CONTROLLED BY MIGHTY COWBOY MORE BANANAS THAN TESCO'S FRUIT COUNTER!

YEEBLE YEEBLE HA!

IF...

GREAT WHITE BIRD MISSILE MORE ACCURATE THAN BLINDFOLDED SHOTPUTTER.....

© Steve Bell 1983

...IN TIME OF HEIGHTENED INTERNATIONAL TENSION, GREAT WHITE BIRD WILL NOT BECOME SITTING DUCK...

© Steve Bell 1983

...GREAT WHITE BIRD WILL EMERGE FROM HOLLOW MOUNTAIN AND GO OUT ON ROAD....

...AND CAUSE TRAFFIC JAM DEEPER, WIDER AND LONGER THAN THE GREATEST RIVER.....

DON'T PANIC!

436.

Tarzan
Born N'Granthambo, Central Africa 1926

After a dazzlingly successful career as a fruit importer, Tarzan of the Apes became interested in politics as a means of recreating, in economic terms, the jungle conditions he knew as a youth, and he joined the Conservative Party.

Always a favourite amongst the wild beasts at party conference time, Tarzan has nonetheless gained a reputation as a closet Wet. This is a false impression, caused by misunderstanding the fact that Tarzan likes to piss on everybody. His interests include wrestling crocodiles and collecting exotic fruit.

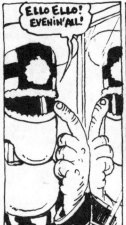

IF... OK, LEFLEGIN, WE'LL TAKE A WALK—BUT REMEMBER—ANY **FUNNY BUSINESS**——I'VE GOT A **SHOOTER!!**

WE GO TO MY HOUSE, YES?

THIS YOUR GAFFE? NICE LITTLE NUMBER!!

...NICE LITTLE FRONTGARDEN!

FUNNY LOOKING BUNCH OF **CONCRETE GNOMES**, THOUGH!

IF... LET ME YINTRODUCE YOU TO GARONYA BAIKAL.... PERHEPS YOU WOULD LIKE CUP OF TEA?

HAVEN'T WE MET BEFORE SOMEWHERE?

AS YOU HEF PRYOBABLY GUESSED CHIEF CONSTABLE— THIS YIS NO ORDINYARY SUBURBAN LIVINKROOM

YIS PURELY A **FRONT**. DO YOU SEE THOSE **BOXES** OVER THERE?

THEY'RE FULL OF **CONCRETE GNOMES**

...**NOT CONCRETE** CHIEF YINSPECTOR...

THOSE GNOMES ARE **SOLID MOSCOW GOLD!!**

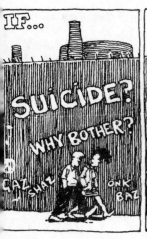

135

136

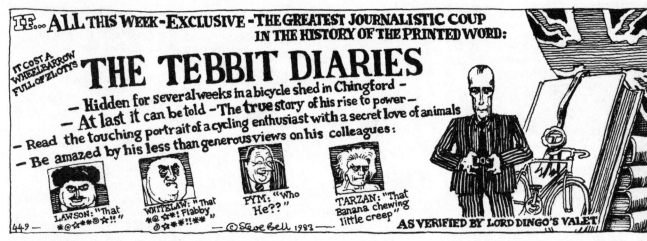

IF... ALL THIS WEEK · EXCLUSIVE · THE GREATEST JOURNALISTIC COUP IN THE HISTORY OF THE PRINTED WORD:

IT COST A WHEELBARROW FULL OF ZLOTYS

THE TEBBIT DIARIES

— Hidden for several weeks in a bicycle shed in Chingford —
— At last it can be told — The **true** story of his rise to power —
— Read the touching portrait of a cycling enthusiast with a secret love of animals
— Be amazed by his less than generous views on his colleagues:

LAWSON: "That *@☆**@☆!!"

WHITELAW: "That *@☆**!!**" Flabby

PYM: "Who He??"

TARZAN: "That Banana chewing little creep"

449 — — ©Steve Bell 1983 — AS VERIFIED BY LORD DINGO'S VALET

IF... THE TEBBIT DIARIES

©Steve Bell 1983

May 1979 – NORMAN TEBBIT, a small time tory MP records his innermost thoughts for posterity:

"At this hour of our victory, I resolve henceforth to keep this diary for the benefit of future generations, but one thing troubles me ...... "

"...should I use pencil or ink? — should I use blue ink or green?? — is my handwriting clear enough for posterity to decipher ??.??"

450.

Tebbit resolves to use a type-writer, but....

"Bad News — I discover it's impossible to NUT one key at a time!"

TOMORROW: TEBBIT'S RISE TO POWER

IF...

THE TEBBIT DIARIES

©Steve Bell 1983

September 1981 — overnight NORMAN TEBBIT is catapulted to prominence when he replaces JAMES PRIOR as EMPLOYMENT SECRETARY.

"Thought I'd be magnanimous and extend a word of condolence to Jim...."

HARD CHEESE, FATS — TOUGH LIFE, EH?

"...But he didn't seem to respond to my friendly advances......."

451.

"I needn't have bothered....."

IF YOU EVER NEED A PLACE ON A YOP SCHEME, YOU KNOW WHERE TO COME, SUNBEAM!

"...henceforth I resolve that I'm not going to waste any more time pussy-footing with pinkos?"

BASTARD! **BASTARD!**

TOMORROW: The TRUTH behind the BIKE speech

IF...

THE TEBBIT DIARIES

October 1981 — his first conference as Employment Secretary, and Tebbit scores a big hit:

...AND, YOU KNOW, HE DIDN'T RIOT...

452.

WINNING THROUGH

...HE GOT ON HIS BIKE AND HE LOOKED FOR WORK!!

©Steve Bell 1983

Tebbit had arrived, but inwardly he began to have doubts:

"....who knows what webs destiny weaves? Will people ever guess that this speech was simply a fortunate slip of the tongue....."

"....in fact I meant to say: "He got in his BUGATTI and looked for workmen to mend his front gate"...."

TOMORROW: Tebbit wins the numbers game

139

Norman Tebbit
Born Castle Grantham, Transylvania 1926

Although it is widely believed that Norman Tebbit began his career as an airline pilot, this story is now acknowledged to be an erroneous interpretation of the real facts, which are that Norman Tebbit is able to transmute into a bat at will.

He joined the Conservative Party dedicated to the single aim of denationalising the blood banks. His interests include meeting young people and flower arranging.

IF... © Steve Bell - 1983

HEY, KIPLING— FETCH ME A CIGAR!... ...I'VE JUST HAD A **GREAT** IDEA!!

SNAP!

IMAGINE **THIS** SCENARIO, REG BABY— **FIVE HUNDRED** PERFORMING PENGUINS PUTTING ON A **PATRIOTIC** PAGEANT!!

WE COULD GET **BIG** ZLOTYS FROM CONSERVATIVE CENTRAL OFFICE TO PUT IT ON... THIS COULD BE **BIG**!...

IT'S GONNA BE **BIGGER** THAN **BIG,** BABE— IT'S GONNA BE **GARGANTUAN!!**

IT'S GONNA HAVE **ROMANCE, VIOLENCE** AND **LUST FOR POWER** AND IT'S GONNA BE CALLED **"SINK THE BELGRANO!!!"**

I CAN SEE IT!

466.

IF... ' **SINK THE BELGRANO'**— A TALE OF HEROISM IN HIGH PLACES— I GOT **FIVE HUNDRED** SINGING DANCING **RELATIVES** FLYING IN ON A **HERCULES** TOMORROW MORNING!

....YEAH, LEW BABY— I GOT A **COOL** QUARTER **MILLION FISH BONDS** UPFRONT FROM THE CONSERVATIVE CAMPAIGN FUND!...

© Steve Bell 1983

NOW I WANNA TALK **VENUES,** SWEETHEART... ...THE **ALBERT HALL** IS OUT YOU SAY?....THE **EMPIRE POOL WEMBLEY** IS A **BIG NIX** ....WHAT THE **HELL**!?! YOU SAY THERE'S ONLY **ONE** POSSIBILITY??

467.

THE ACOUSTICS ARE **LOUSY,** BUT I'LL TAKE IT!!

IF...

Panel 1:
OH, THE PRIVATISED DUSTCART IS-A-COMIN' ON OVER THE HILL!!

DARLING — YOU SOUND SO RESOLUTE I COULD ALMOST WEEP!!

© Steve Bell 1983

Panel 2:
GATHER ROUND BOYS + GIRLS — THIS IS THE BIG PRODUCTION NUMBER!!!

470.

Panel 3:
THE HILLS ARE ALIVE WITH THE STENCH OF GUANO... ...WITH OLD ARGIE MINES BLOWING SHEEP TO BITS!!

LA LA LA LA!!

ECSTASY ECSTASY!!

IF...

Panel 4:
GRAND FINALE, SUNG TO THE TUNE OF "OKLAHOMA!"

FO-O-O-O-OR-TRESS FALKLANDS WHERE THE CASH GOES POURIN' DOWN THE DRAIN...

Panel 5:
WHERE THE SOUND OF SHEEP WILL MAKE YOU WEEP AND THE DRIZZLE COMES RIGHT BEHIND THE RAIN!!

471.

Panel 6:
-FOR-TRESS
-FALKLANDS
-FORTRESS
-FALKLANDS
-FORTRESS
-FALKLANDS
-FORTRESS
-FALKLANDS

WE KNOW WE BELONG TO THE LAND!!...
....
AND THE LAND WE BELONG TO is MINED!!

© Steve Bell 1983

Panel 7:
SO IF YOU WANNA PAY A BILLION POUNDS A DAY TO SHOWCASE ALL YOUR WEAPONS ON A ROCK FULL OF PENGUINS—FORTRESS FALKLANDS is O.K!!

YEE HA!!

BAM

150

IF...
THE
TEBBIT
DIARIES
Continued

IT'S THE
REAL THING!

Norman Tebby!

MAY 1983 —
"Election time is here again, and of course the mud is beginning to fly. I can't think why these people become so abusive...."

"...I just ignore them altogether — and that's just what these left wing types can't abide!
It's an old trick I learnt many years ago when I was a young whippersnapper!"

©SteveBell

"Y'know, to hear some of these professed pinkos go on about my attitude to youth unemployment, you'd think I'd never been young myself. I often cast my mind back to the day I entered the world of work..."

"...as a fresh faced young graduate of the Bela Lugosi Charm School in downtown Walthamstow"

SLEEK

1983   472

IF₀₀₀₀
the
TEBBIT
DIARIES

"I learnt a thing or two at Charm School I can tell you — and one of the most useful things I learnt there was how to make an impression at cocktail parties....."

"...they used to confront us with potentially socially delicate situations. For instance, how does one cope when one has a plate of canapés in one hand, a drink & perhaps a cigarette in the other, and one has to open a door for a lady...."

"....it's so simple when one knows the correct social technique!"

473.

©SteveBell 1983

SHOVE

151

IF...

THE TEBBIT DIARIES

"Election time means pressing the flesh — I suppose it has to be done, but I must say it brings problems of its own"

© Steve Bell 1983

NEXT?

GOOD LORD! HE BIT ME!!

"...the trouble is that I sometimes get a little carried away once I get a taste for it....."

"...I must say I do like all the traditional trappings of a good vigorous campaign...."

STOP IT NORMAN! STAY AWAY FROM THAT BABY!!

RRRRR!

LUNGE

MADAM GET BACK!

476.

NO!! NO!! UUURRRGH!!

IF...

THE TEBBIT DIARIES

© Steve Bell 1983

"And so the campaign goes on out on the street..."

SO PLEASED TO MEET YOU...

"...I get the oddest requests sometimes, and from the oddest people....."

MY YOU'RE A CLEVER LITTLE CHAP. OF COURSE YOU CAN!

MAY I HAVE YOUR **AUTOGRAPH** MR. TEBBIT, SIR??

CONGRATULATIONS, **NORM!** YOU'VE JUST SIGNED THIS DOCUMENT!!

FOAM FOAM

477.

I PLEDGE THAT:
- I WILL DO FOR EMPLOYMENT WHAT ATTILA THE HUN DID FOR HORTICULTURE.
- I WILL ENCOURAGE THE RETURN OF VICTORIAN VALUES - MOST NOTABLY HYPOCRISY, GREED, AND MASS IGNORANCE
- ANY OBJECTORS SHOULD NOTE THAT I AM IN ALL PROBABILITY GOING TO BE MADE HOME SECRETARY WHICH MEANS THAT ALL THE OLD BILL ALL THE NICKS, AND ALL THE SLAMMERS ARE GOING TO BE MY MANOR SQUIRE KNOW WHAT I MEAN

Norm Tebby

153

© Steve Bell 1983. 482

© Steve Bell 1983 ·483·

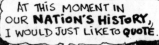

486

AT THIS MOMENT IN OUR **NATION'S HISTORY**, I WOULD JUST LIKE TO **QUOTE**...

...THE **WORDS** OF SAINT MICHAEL SPILLANE: "YOU COMMIE PUNKS, YOU BLEEDING HEARTS — — I'M GONNA CRAP ON YOU ALL FROM A GREAT HEIGHT!"

© Steve Bell 1983

I HAVE A **VISION**.

485

...A **VISION** OF THE **FUTURE** — A **VISION** OF THE **KIND** OF WORLD WE **ALL** WISH TO SEE...

...IN THE **WORDS** OF THE **HARRODS PROPERTY CATALOGUE**....

"HOME COUNTIES, LARGE MANOR HOUSE, 25 RECEPTION ROOMS, 19 BEDROOMS, 19 BATHROOMS, TENNIS COURTS, SWIMMING POOLS, 300 ACRES, OBLIGING PEASANTRY, £4½ MILLION O.N.O." — ISN'T THAT A **BEAUTIFUL THOUGHT**?

© Steve Bell - 1983 -

158

Margaret Thatcher
Forged Grantham, Lincs
1926

The issue of the coupling of Thor, God of Thunder and a mothballed Dreadnought, Marghilda, or the Iron Lady, as she is more widely known, is a deeply caring and sensitive individual committed with every fibre of her being to the total and complete eradication of Socialism from the face of the planet. To this end, it is a known fact that she has not slept for over fifty-seven years. Her interests include rolling back the frontiers of the State, abolishing Socialism and remaining in Power for ever.